This book belongs to

_____

There are 50 autographs and photos to collect.
Can you find them all?

Hint: Each character only appears in certain parks. Use the pictures to help you find them.

Checklist ☑

1. Aladdin and Jasmine ☐
2. Alice ☐
3. Anastasia and Drizella ☐
4. Anna ☐
5. Ariel ☐
6. Aurora ☐
7. Belle ☐
8. Bo Peep and Woody ☐
9. Buzz ☐
10. Captain Jack Sparrow ☐
11. Chip and Dale ☐
12. Cinderella ☐
13. Daisy ☐
14. Doc McStuffins ☐
15. Donald ☐
16. Edna Mode ☐

17. Elsa ☐
18. Fairy Godmother ☐
19. Fancy Nancy ☐
20. Gaston ☐
21. Goofy ☐
22. Green Army Man ☐
23. Joy and Sadness ☐
24. Launchpad McQuack ☐
25. Mary Poppins ☐
26. Merida ☐
27. Mickey ☐
28. Mike and Sulley ☐
29. Minnie ☐
30. Mulan ☐
31. Olaf ☐
32. Peter Pan ☐

33. Pluto ☐
34. Pocahontas ☐
35. Ralph and Venellope ☐
36. Rapunzel ☐
37. Russell and Dug ☐
38. Scrooge McDuck ☐
39. Snow White ☐
40. Stitch ☐
41. Suzy and Perla ☐
42. Tiana ☐
43. Tigger and Pooh ☐
44. Tinker Bell ☐
45. Tweedle Dee and Tweedle Dum ☐
46. Vampirina ☐

PHOTOs ONLY
47. Baymax ☐
48. BB-8 ☐
49. Chewbacca ☐
50. Kylo Ren ☐

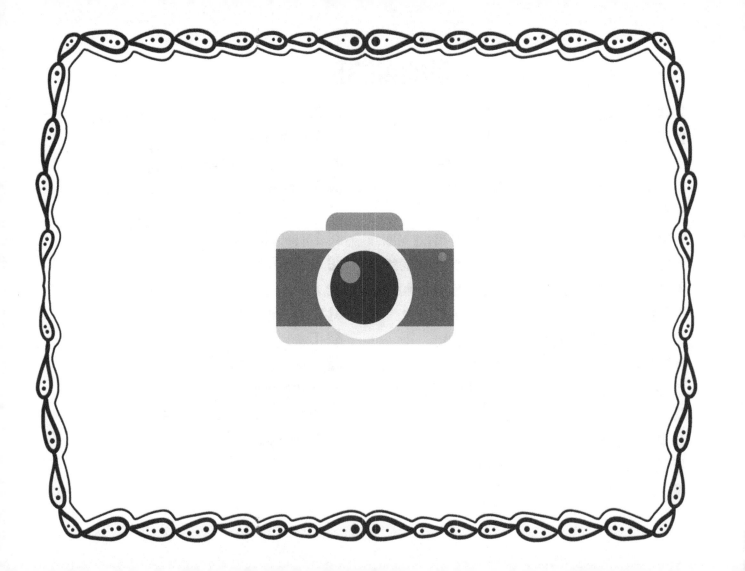

Aladdin and Jasmine

Alice

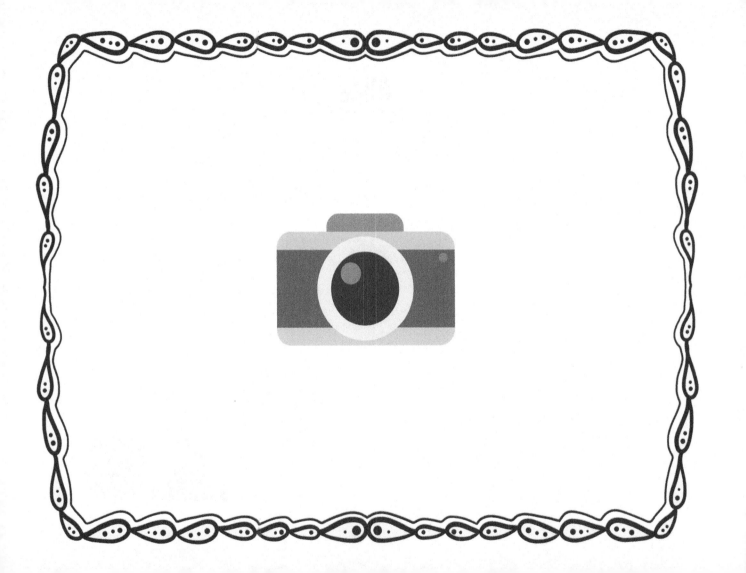

Anastasia and Drizella

Anna

Ariel

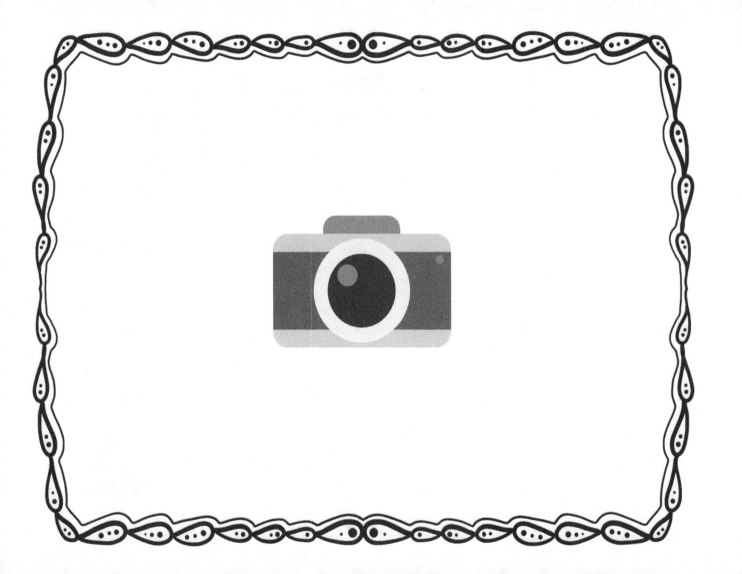

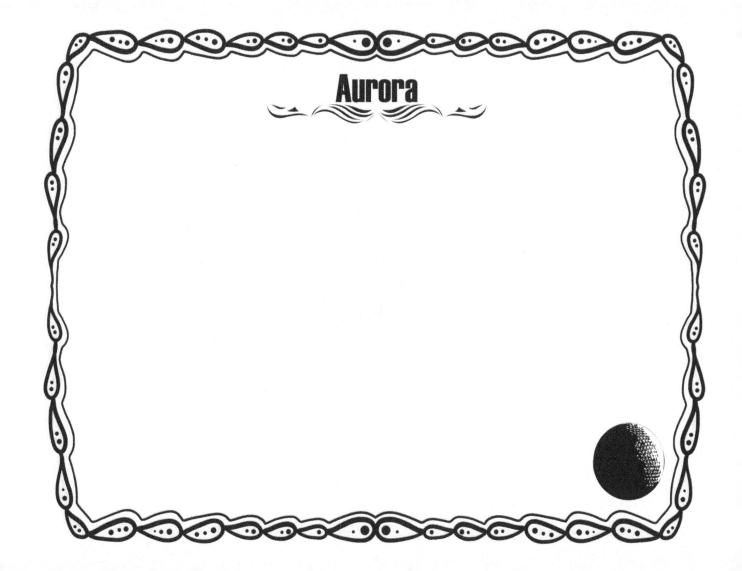

Aurora

Belle

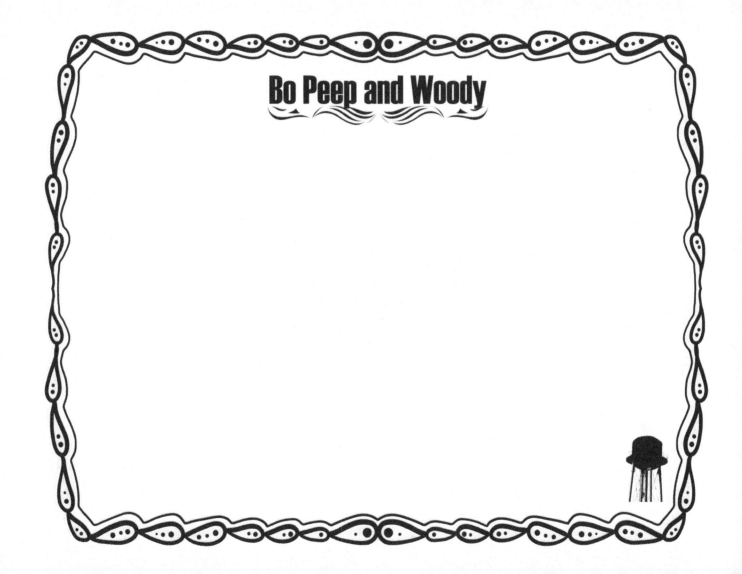

Bo Peep and Woody

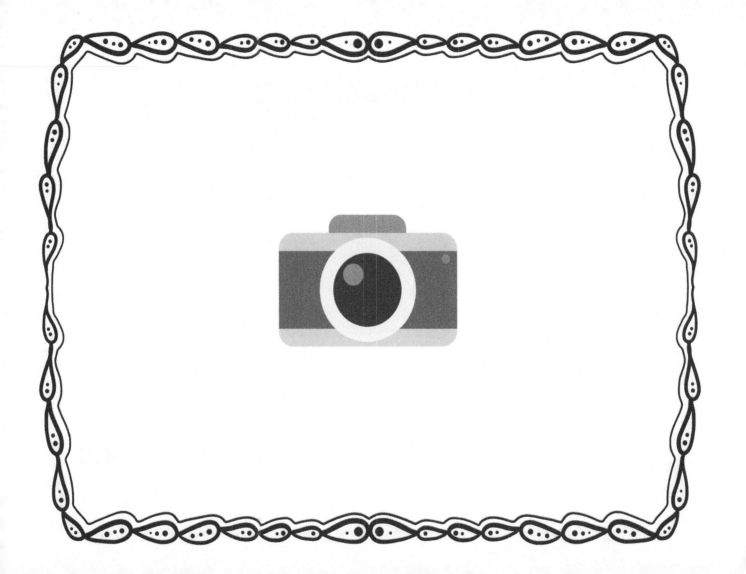

Buzz

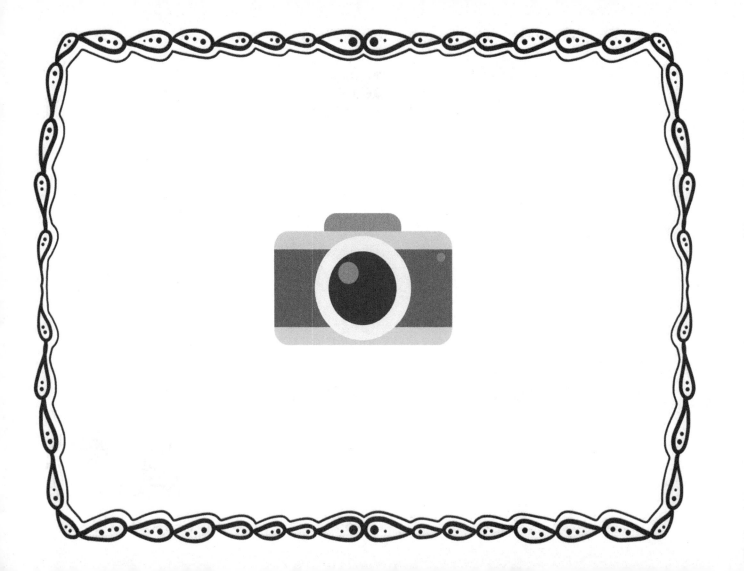

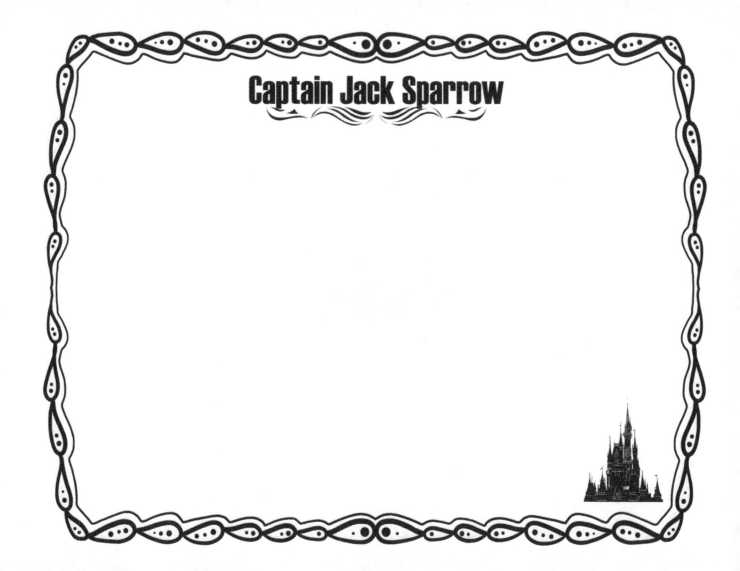

Captain Jack Sparrow

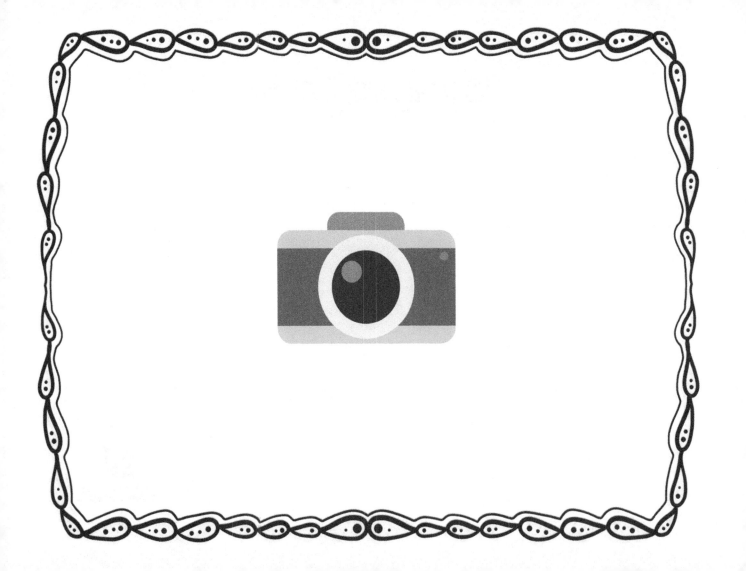

Chip and Dale

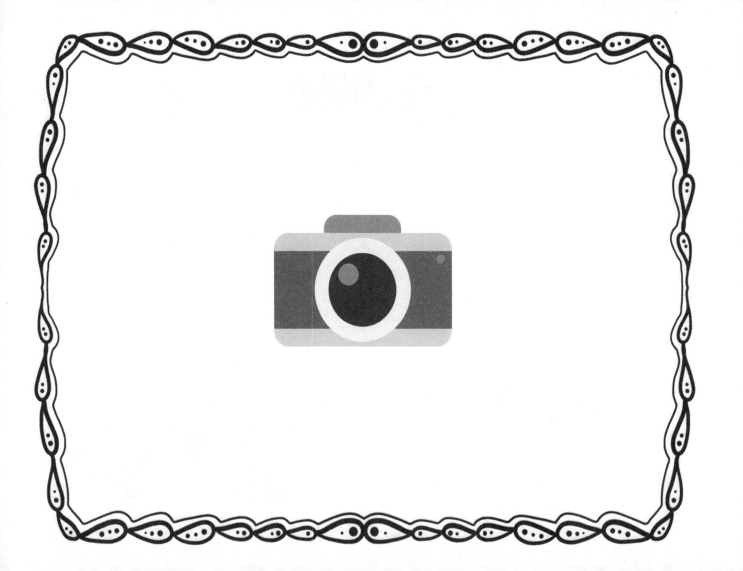

Cinderella

Daisy

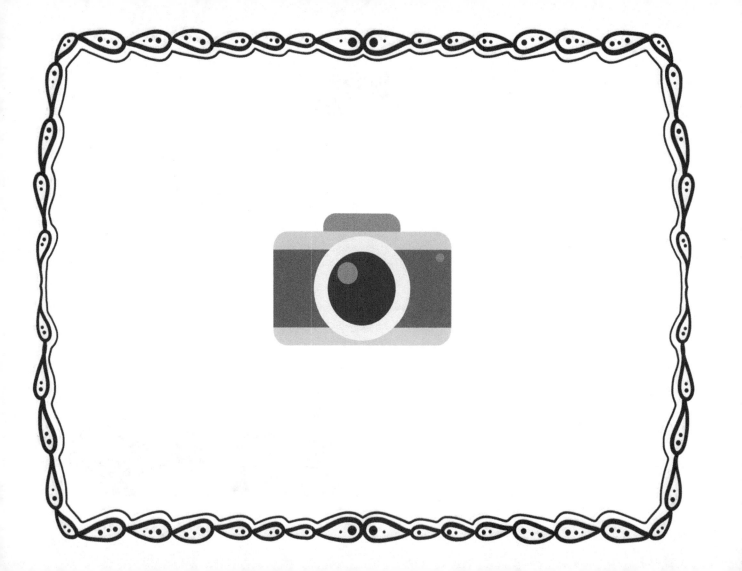

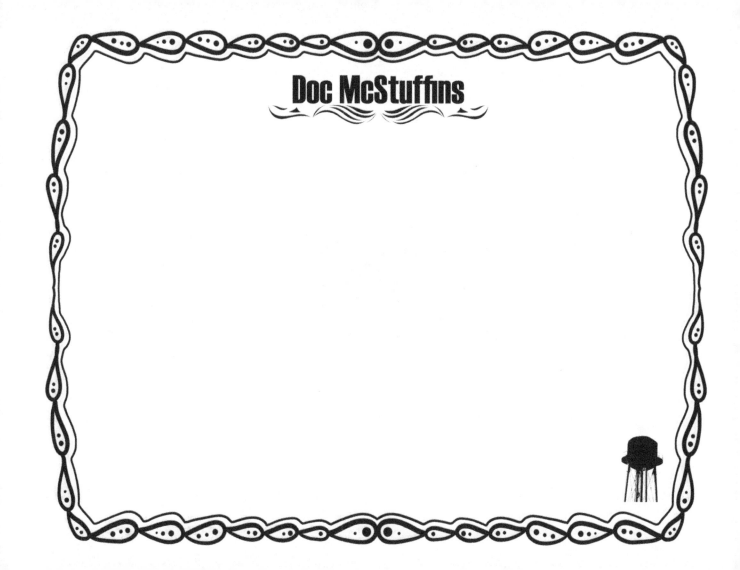

Doc McStuffins

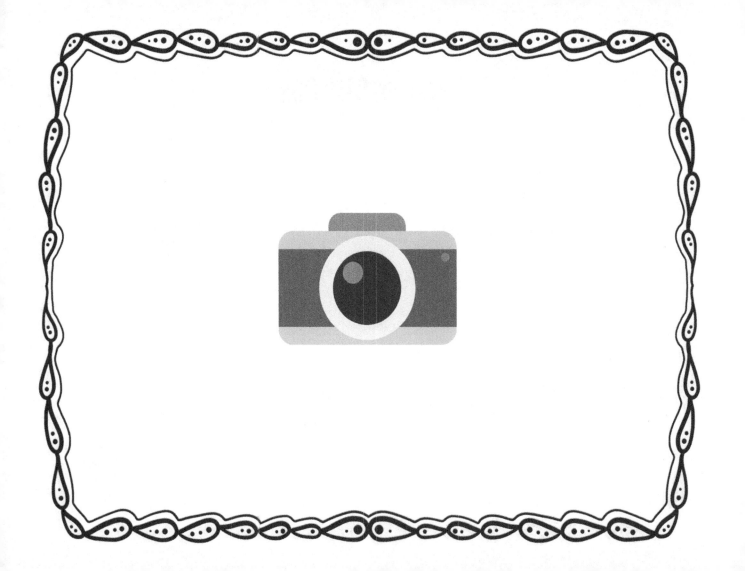

Donald

Edna Mode

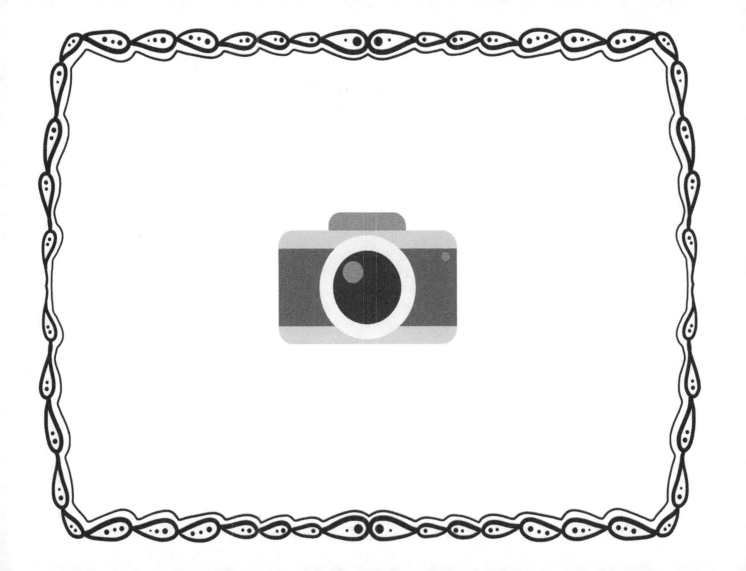

Elsa

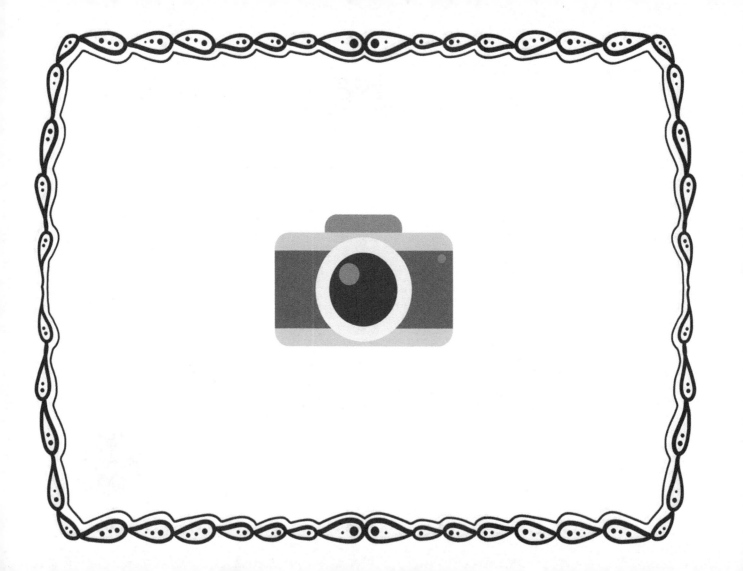

Fairy Godmother

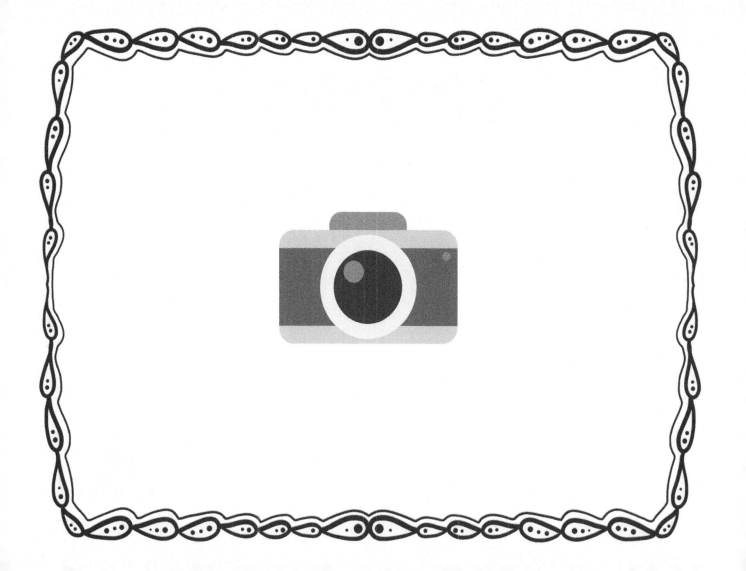

Fancy Nancy

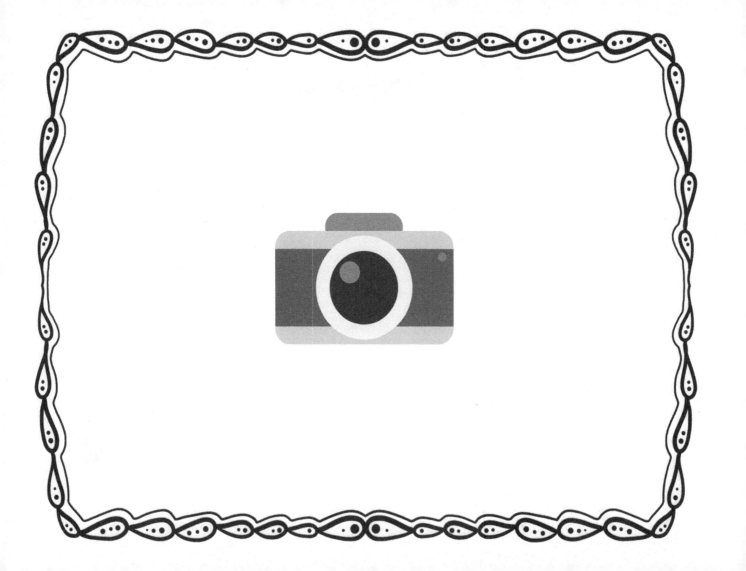

Gaston

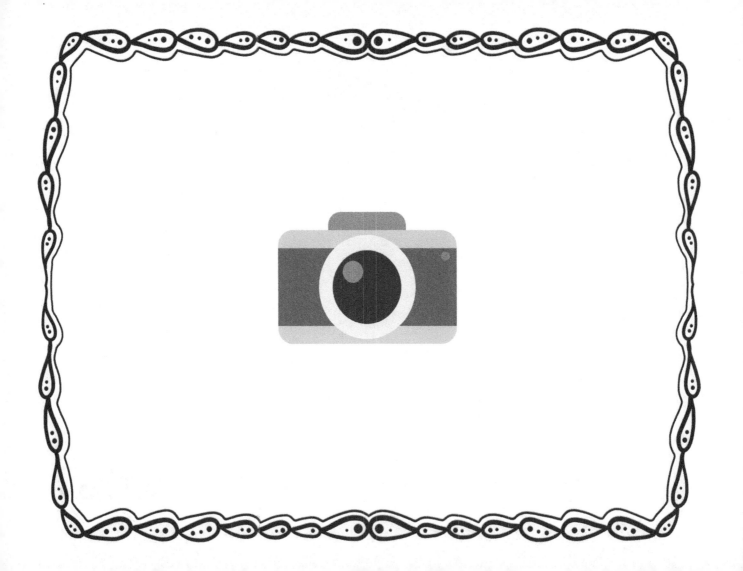

Goofy

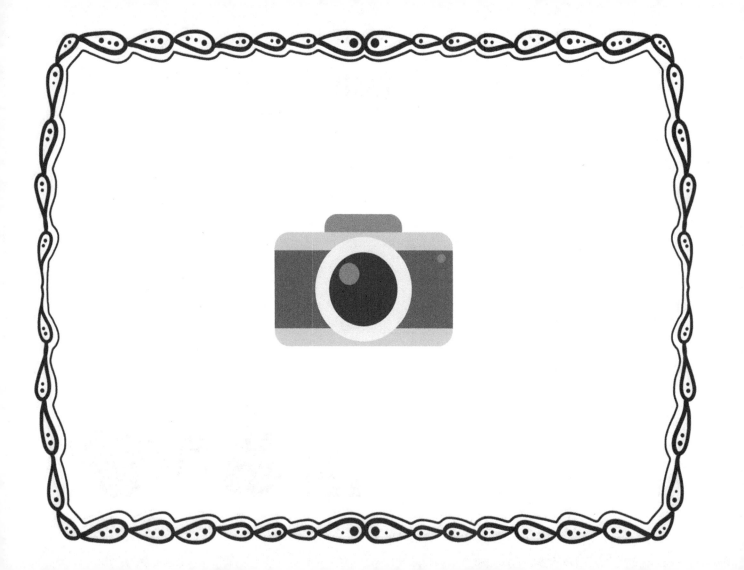

Green Army Man

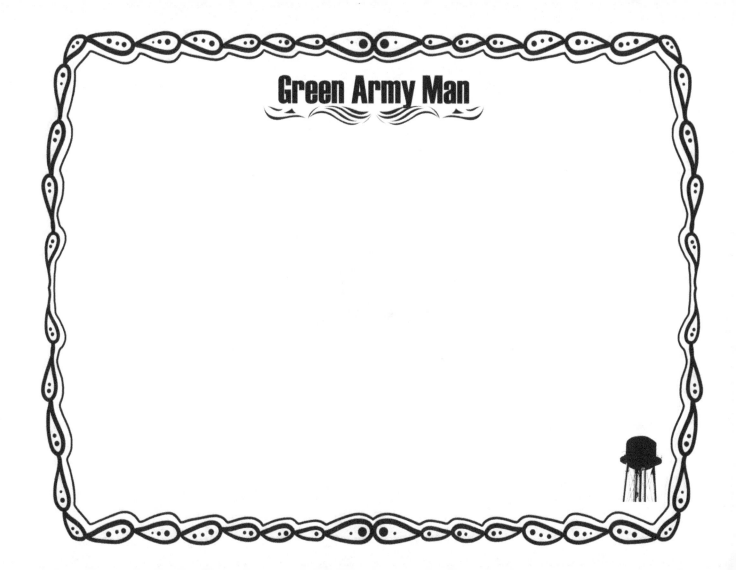

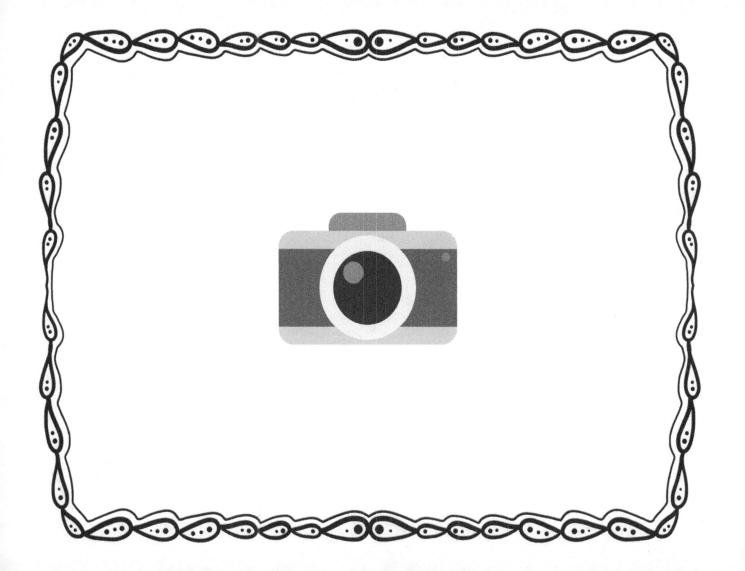

Joy and Sadness

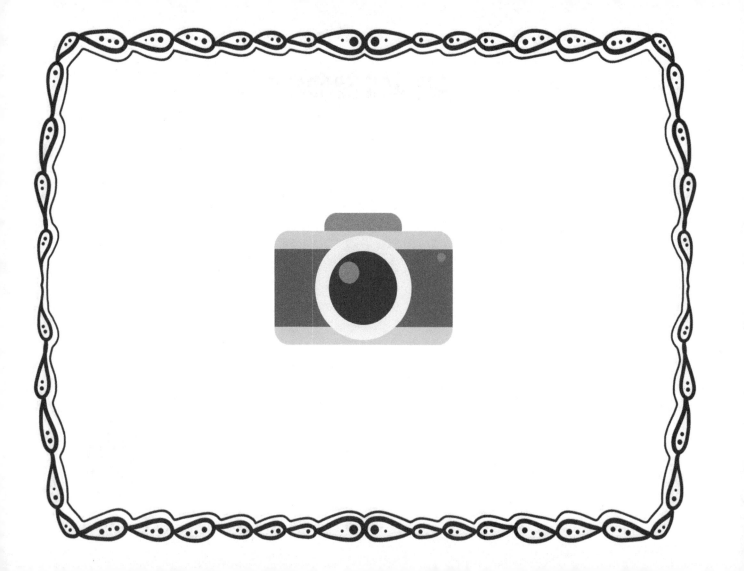

Launchpad McQuack

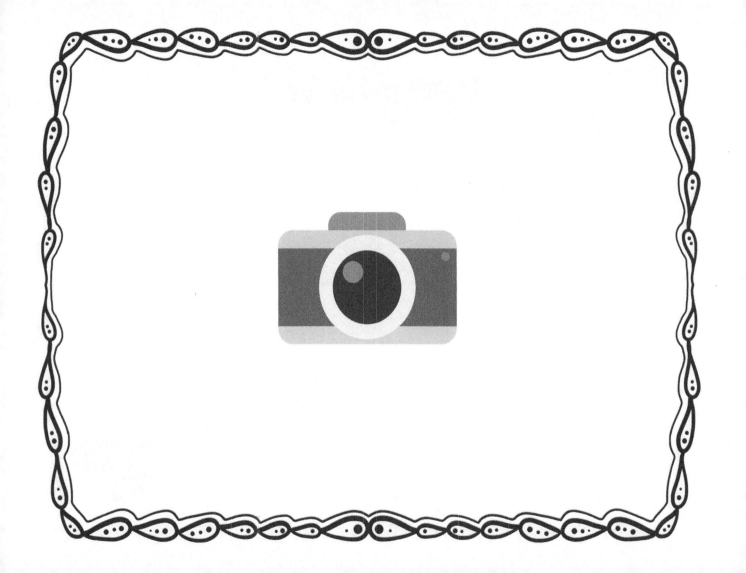

Mary Poppins

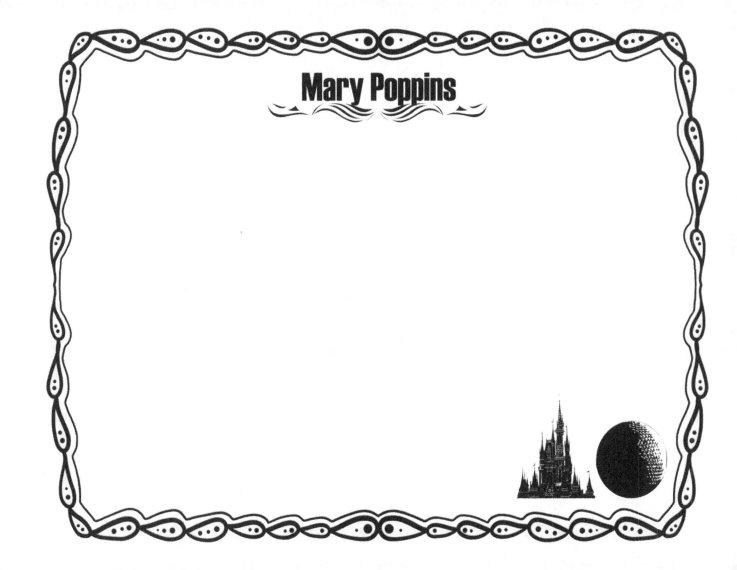

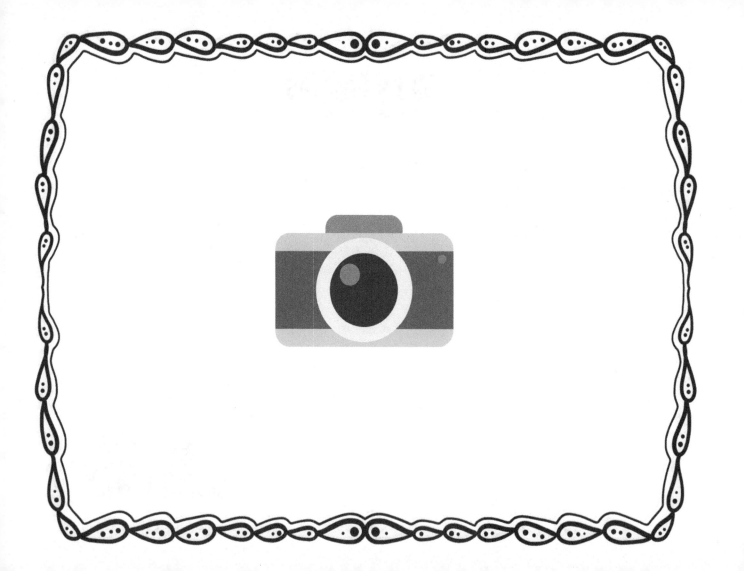

Merida

Mickey

Mike and Sulley

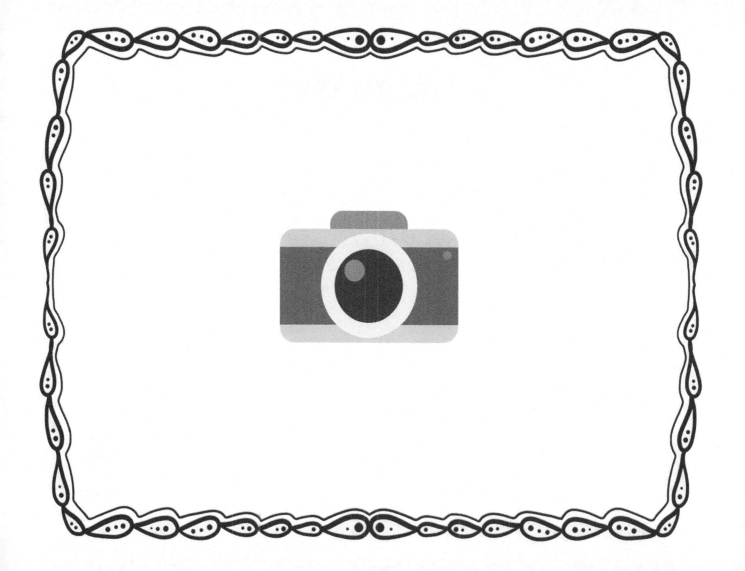

Minnie

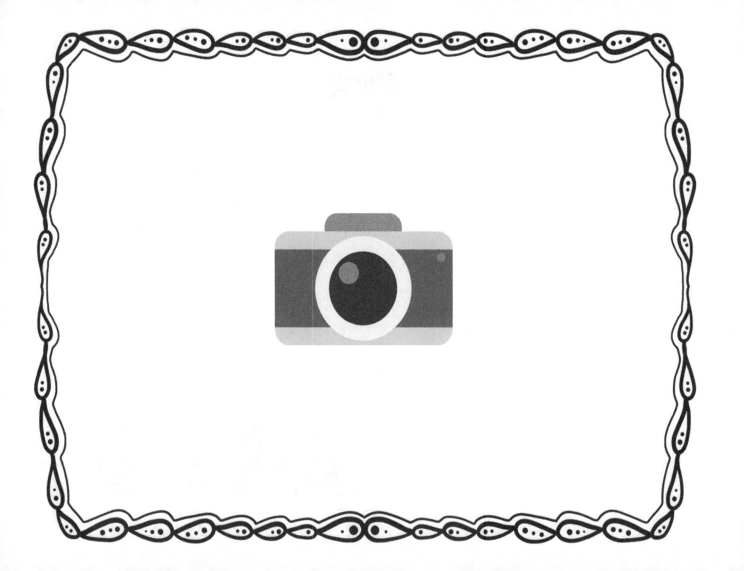

Mulan

Olaf

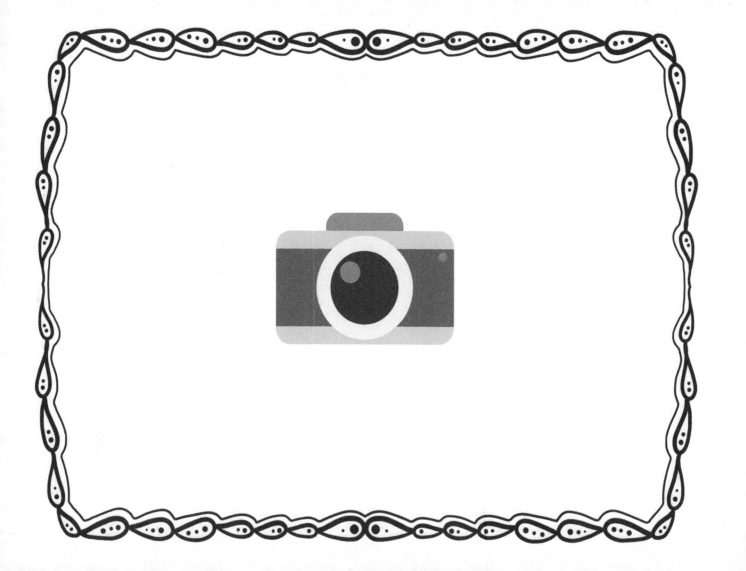

Peter Pan

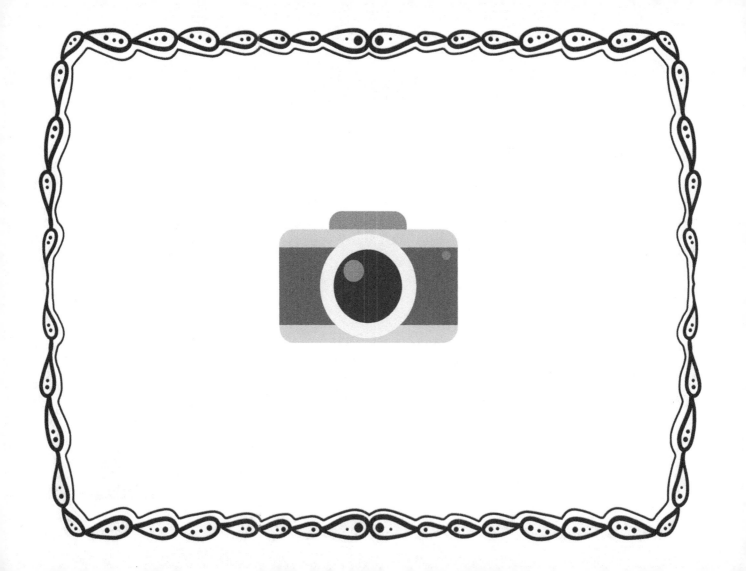

Pluto

Pocahontas

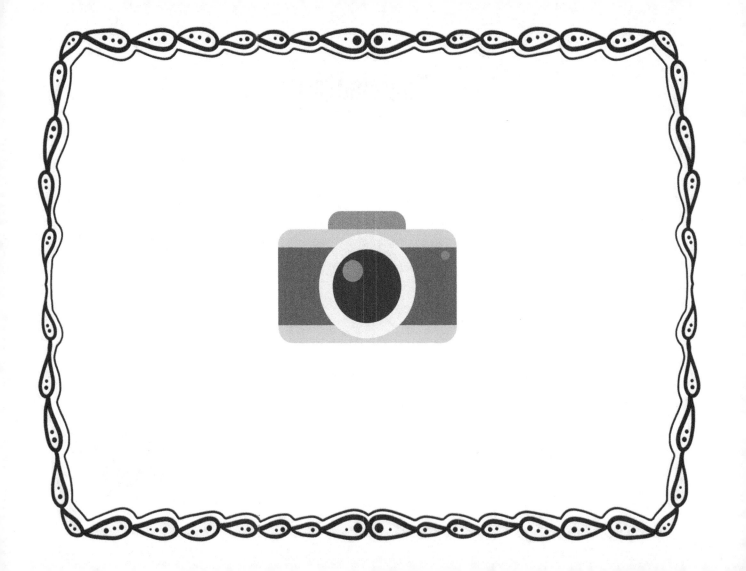

Ralph and Venellope

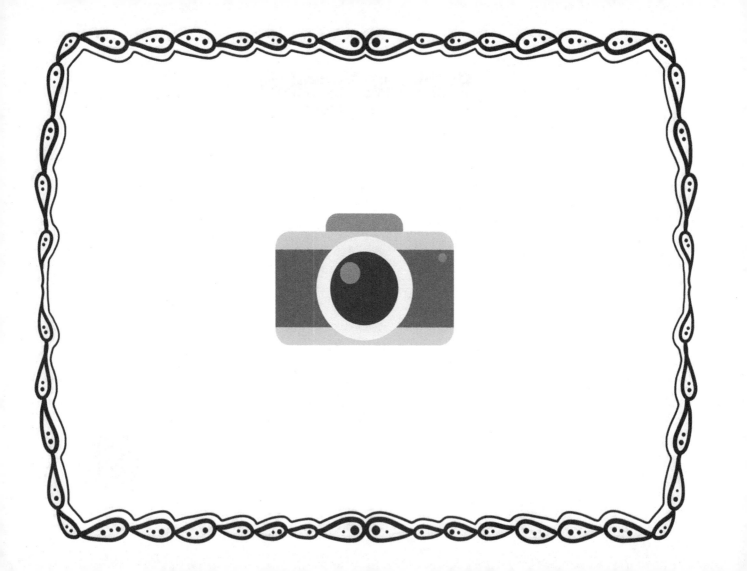

Rapunzel

Russell and Dug

Scrooge McDuck

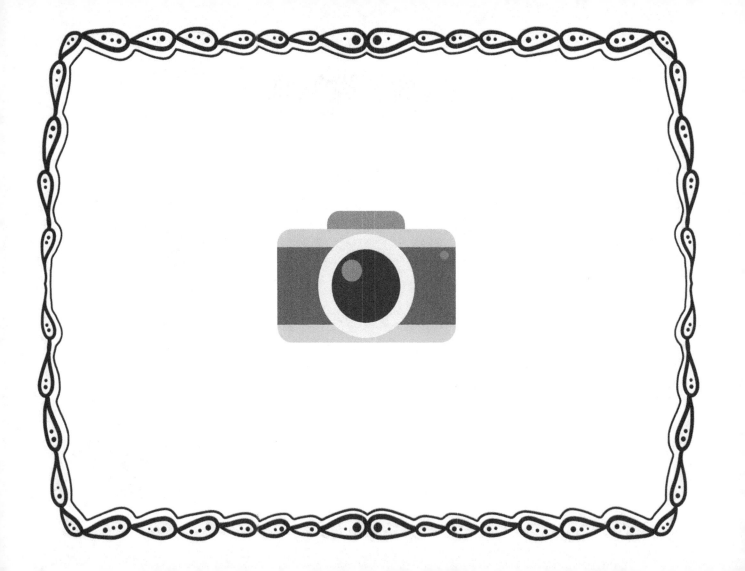

Snow White

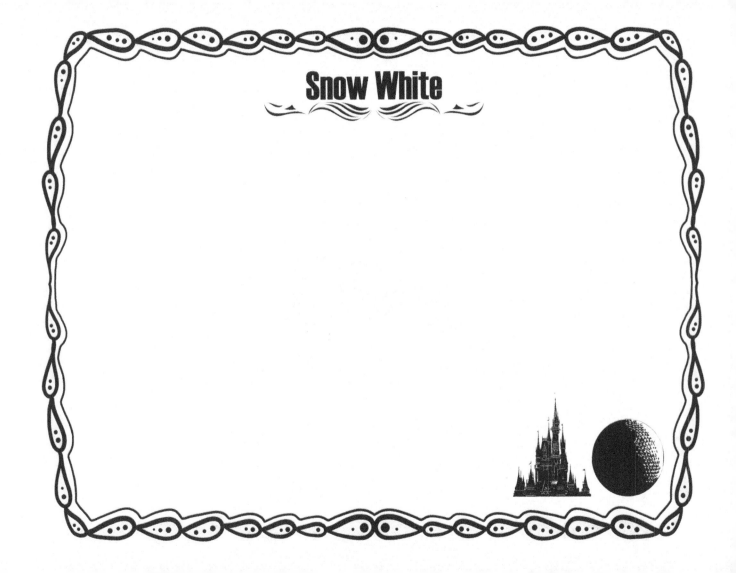

Stitch

Suzy and Perla

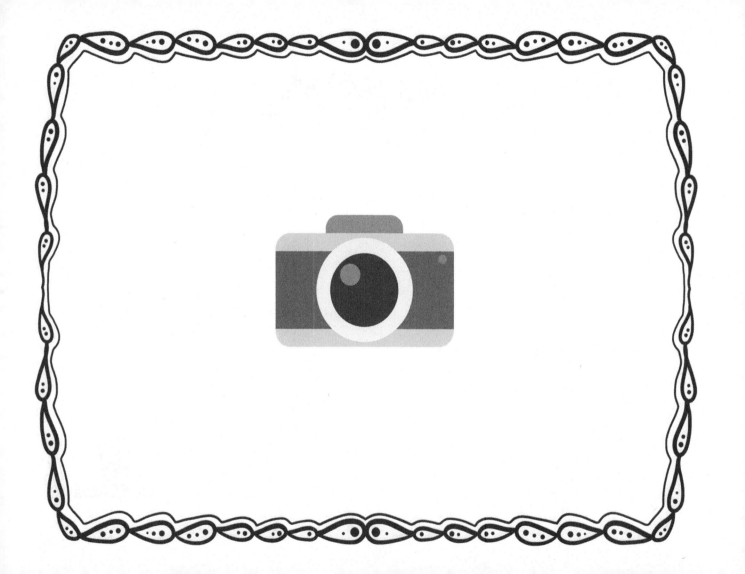

Tiana

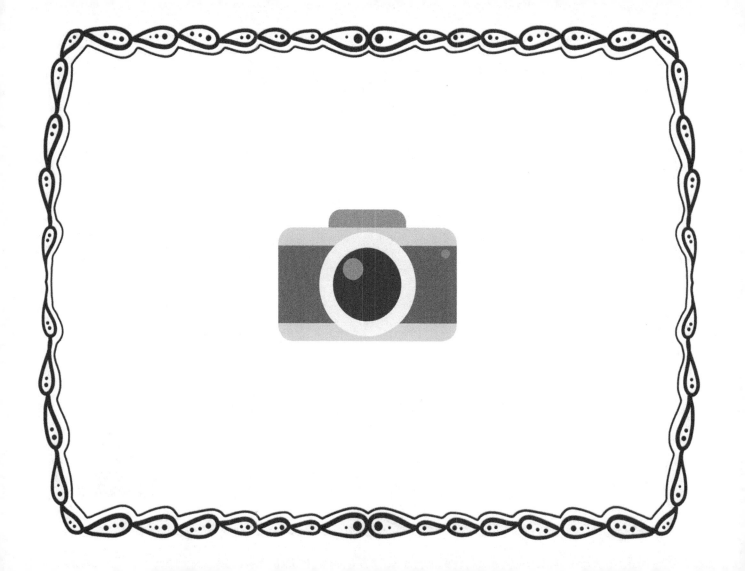

Tigger and Pooh

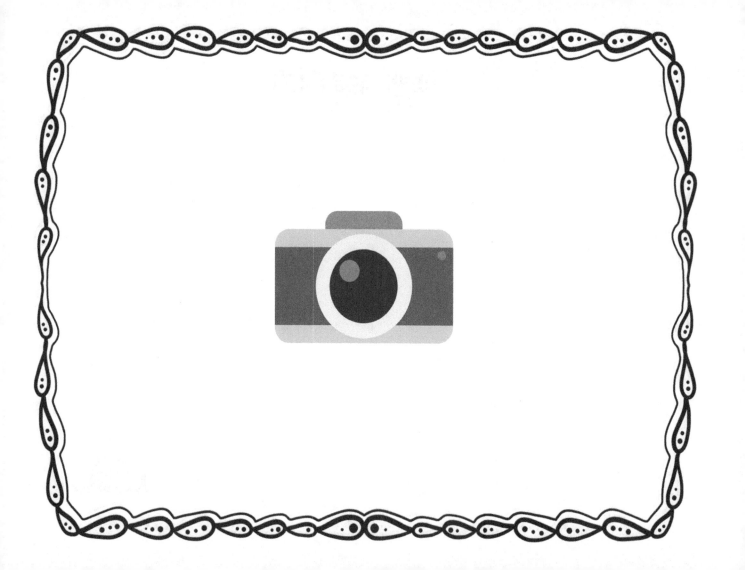

Tinker Bell

Tweedle Dee and Tweedle Dum

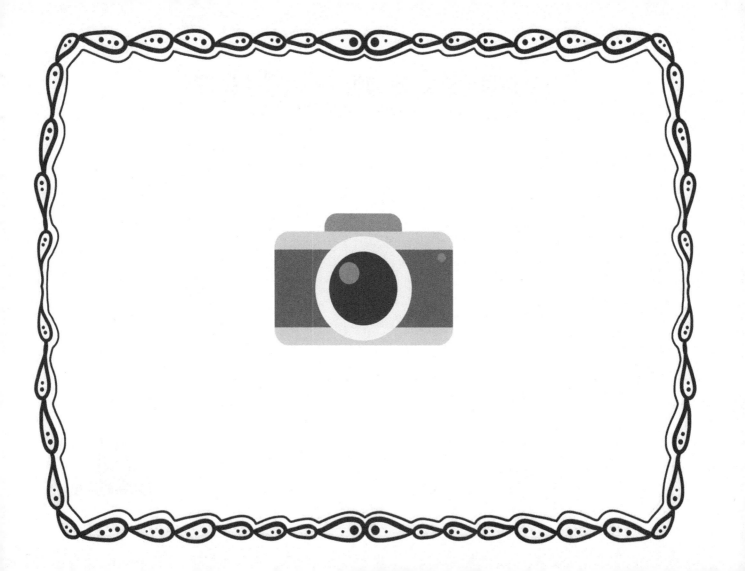

Vampirina

Baymax

BB-8

Chewbacca

Kylo Ren

Bonus Page

Bonus Page

Bonus Page

Bonus Page

Bonus Page